In 202

Be: ....

....

Quit: ....

....

Continue: ....

....

Try: ....

....

Learn: ....

....

Start: ....

....

Have: ....

....

Stop: ....

....

JANUARY 2022

Sunday	Monday	Tuesday
2	3	4
9	10	11
16	Martin Luther King Jr. Day 17	18
23	24	25
30	31	

Wednesday	Thursday	Friday	Saturday
			New Year's Day 1
5	6	7	8
12	13	14	15
19	20	21	22
26	27	28	29

January
at a glance

January Goals:

January Birthdays:

January Anniversaries:

January To Do:

- ○
- ○
- ○
- ○
- ○
- ○
- ○
- ○
- ○

Habit Tracker

Habit	1	2	3	4	5	6	7	8	9	10	11	12	13

Today could be day one or just one day

Gratitude:

Shopping List:

Budget:

14	15	16	17	18	19	20	21	22	23	24	25	26	27	28	29	30	31

January 2022

Monday, 27

Movement:

Meals:

Tuesday, 28

Movement:

Meals:

Wednesday, 29

Movement:

Meals:

Thursday, 30

Movement:

Meals:

Happy + Healthy Intention:

Movement:

Meals:

Friday, 31

Movement:

Meals:

Saturday, 1

Movement:

Meals:

Sunday, 2

Grocery Must Haves:

January 2022

Monday, 3

Movement:

Meals:

Tuesday, 4

Movement:

Meals:

Wednesday, 5

Movement:

Meals:

Thursday, 6

Movement:

Meals:

Happy + Healthy Intention:

Movement:

Meals:

Friday, 7

Movement:

Meals:

Saturday, 8

Movement:

Meals:

Sunday, 9

Grocery Must Haves:

January 2022

Monday, 10

-
-
-
-

Movement:

Meals:

Tuesday, 11

-
-
-
-

Movement:

Meals:

Wednesday, 12

-
-
-
-

Movement:

Meals:

Thursday, 13

-
-
-
-

Movement:

Meals:

Happy + Healthy Intention:

Friday, 14

Movement:

Meals:

Saturday, 15

Movement:

Meals:

Sunday, 16

Movement:

Meals:

Grocery Must Haves:

January 2022

Monday, 17

•
•
•
•

Movement:

Meals:

Tuesday, 18

•
•
•
•

Movement:

Meals:

Wednesday, 19

•
•
•
•

Movement:

Meals:

Thursday, 20

•
•
•
•

Movement:

Meals:

Happy + Healthy Intention:

Friday, 21

Movement:

Meals:

Saturday, 22

Movement:

Meals:

Sunday, 23

Movement:

Meals:

Grocery Must Haves:

January 2022

Monday, 24

•
•
•
•

Movement:

Meals:

Tuesday, 25

•
•
•
•

Movement:

Meals:

Wednesday, 26

•
•
•
•

Movement:

Meals:

Thursday, 27

•
•
•
•

Movement:

Meals:

Happy + Healthy Intention:

Friday, 28

- DAY 5 Bootcamp.
- ♥ WON Boot camp challange
- linda Ross MP Sign up.
-

Movement:

Meals: proteinshake
-ham lunch
-Orange chicken

Saturday, 29

-
-
-

Movement:

Meals:

Sunday, 30

-
-
-

Movement:

Meals:

Grocery Must Haves:

○ ○ ○
○ ○ ○
○ ○ ○
○ ○ ○
○ ○ ○

January 2022

Monday, 31

-
-
-
-

Movement:

Meals:

Tuesday, 1

-
-
-
-

Movement:

Meals:

Wednesday, 2

-
-
-
-

Movement:

Meals:

Thursday, 3

-
-
-
-

Movement:

Meals:

Happy + Healthy Intention:

Movement:

Meals:

Friday, 4

Movement:

Meals:

Saturday, 5

Movement:

Meals:

Sunday, 6

Grocery Must Haves:

FEBRUARY 2022

Sunday	Monday	Tuesday
		1
6	7	8
13	Valentine's Day 14	15
20	Presidents' Day 21	22
27	28	

Wednesday	Thursday	Friday	Saturday
2	3	4	5
9	10	11	12
16	17	18	19
23	24	25	26

February
at a glance

February Goals:

February Birthdays:

February Anniversaries:

February To Do:

- ○
- ○
- ○
- ○
- ○
- ○
- ○
- ○
- ○

Habit Tracker

Habit	1	2	3	4	5	6	7	8	9	10

Change is a slow, beautiful process

Gratitude:

Shopping List:

Budget:

11	12	13	14	15	16	17	18	19	20	21	22	23	24	25	26	27	28

February 2022

Monday, 7

•
•
•
•

Movement:

Meals:

Tuesday, 8

•
•
•
•

Movement:

Meals:

Wednesday, 9

•
•
•
•

Movement:

Meals:

Thursday, 10

•
•
•
•

Movement:

Meals:

Happy + Healthy Intention:

Movement:

Meals:

Friday, 11

Movement:

Meals:

Saturday, 12

Movement:

Meals:

Sunday, 13

Grocery Must Haves:

February 2022

Monday, 14

-
-
-
-

Movement:

Meals:

Tuesday, 15

-
-
-
-

Movement:

Meals:

Wednesday, 16

-
-
-
-

Movement:

Meals:

Thursday, 17

-
-
-
-

Movement:

Meals:

Happy + Healthy Intention:

Friday, 18

Movement:

Meals:

Saturday, 19

Movement:

Meals:

Sunday, 20

Movement:

Meals:

Grocery Must Haves:

February 2022

Monday, 21

•
•
•
•

Movement:

Meals:

Tuesday, 22

•
•
•
•

Movement:

Meals:

Wednesday, 23

•
•
•
•

Movement:

Meals:

Thursday, 24

•
•
•
•

Movement:

Meals:

Happy + Healthy Intention:

Friday, 25

Movement:

Meals:

Saturday, 26

Movement:

Meals:

Sunday, 27

Movement:

Meals:

Grocery Must Haves:

February 2022

Monday, 28

•
•
•
•

Movement:

Meals:

Tuesday, 1

•
•
•
•

Movement:

Meals:

Wednesday, 2

•
•
•
•

Movement:

Meals:

Thursday, 3

•
•
•
•

Movement:

Meals:

Happy + Healthy Intention:

Friday, 4

Movement:

Meals:

Saturday, 5

Movement:

Meals:

Sunday, 6

Movement:

Meals:

Grocery Must Haves:

MARCH 2022

Sunday	Monday	Tuesday
		1
6	7	8 International Women's Day
13	14	15
20	21	22
27	28	29

Wednesday	Thursday	Friday	Saturday
2	3	4	5
9	10	11	12
16	Saint Patrick's Day 17	18	19
23	24	25	26
30	31		

March
at a glance

March Goals:

March Birthdays:

March Anniversaries:

March To Do:

○
○
○
○
○
○
○
○
○

Habit Tracker

Habit	1	2	3	4	5	6	7	8	9	10	11	12	13

Actually, life is beautiful and I have time

Gratitude:

Shopping List:

Budget:

14	15	16	17	18	19	20	21	22	23	24	25	26	27	28	29	30	31

March 2022

Monday, 7

•
•
•
•

Movement:

Meals:

Tuesday, 8

•
•
•
•

Movement:

Meals:

Wednesday, 9

•
•
•
•

Movement:

Meals:

Thursday, 10

•
•
•
•

Movement:

Meals:

Happy + Healthy Intention:

Friday, 11

Movement:

Meals:

Saturday, 12

Movement:

Meals:

Sunday, 13

Movement:

Meals:

Grocery Must Haves:

March 2022

Monday, 14

•
•
•
•

Movement:

Meals:

Tuesday, 15

•
•
•
•

Movement:

Meals:

Wednesday, 16

•
•
•
•

Movement:

Meals:

Thursday, 17

•
•
•
•

Movement:

Meals:

Happy + Healthy Intention:

Friday, 18

Movement:

Meals:

Saturday, 19

Movement:

Meals:

Sunday, 20

Movement:

Meals:

Grocery Must Haves:

March 2022

Monday, 21

-
-
-
-

Movement:

Meals:

Tuesday, 22

-
-
-
-

Movement:

Meals:

Wednesday, 23

-
-
-
-

Movement:

Meals:

Thursday, 24

-
-
-
-

Movement:

Meals:

Happy + Healthy Intention:

Friday, 25

Movement:

Meals:

Saturday, 26

Movement:

Meals:

Sunday, 27

Movement:

Meals:

Grocery Must Haves:

March 2022

Monday, 28

•
•
•
•

Movement:

Meals:

Tuesday, 29

•
•
•
•

Movement:

Meals:

Wednesday, 30

•
•
•
•

Movement:

Meals:

Thursday, 31

•
•
•
•

Movement:

Meals:

Happy + Healthy Intention:

Friday, 1

Movement:

Meals:

Saturday, 2

Movement:

Meals:

Sunday, 3

Movement:

Meals:

Grocery Must Haves:

Spring 2022

Be:

Quit:

Continue:

Try:

Learn:

Start:

Have:

Stop:

Quarterly Check In

What worked over the last few months?

What did not work over the last few months?

Which goal do I want to focus on this quarter?

What steps do I need to take?

How do I want to feel like at the next quarterly check in?

APRIL 2022

Sunday	Monday	Tuesday
3	4	5
10	11	12
Easter 17	18	19
24	25	26

Wednesday	Thursday	Friday	Saturday
		Ramadan Begins 1	2
6	7	8	9
13	14	15	16
20	21	Earth Day 22	23
27	28	29	Ramadan Ends 30

at a glance

April Goals:

April Birthdays:

April Anniversaries:

April To Do:

○
○
○
○
○
○
○
○
○

Habit Tracker

Habit	1	2	3	4	5	6	7	8	9	10	11	12

Wonderful things will find their way to you

Gratitude:

Shopping List:

Budget:

13	14	15	16	17	18	19	20	21	22	23	24	25	26	27	28	29	30

April 2022

Monday, 4

Movement:

Meals:

Tuesday, 5

Movement:

Meals:

Wednesday, 6

Movement:

Meals:

Thursday, 7

Movement:

Meals:

Happy + Healthy Intention:

Movement:

Meals:

Friday, 8

Movement:

Meals:

Saturday, 9

Movement:

Meals:

Sunday, 10

Grocery Must Haves:

April 2022

Monday, 11

Movement:

Meals:

Tuesday, 12

Movement:

Meals:

Wednesday, 13

Movement:

Meals:

Thursday, 14

Movement:

Meals:

Happy + Healthy Intention:

Friday, 15

Movement:

Meals:

Saturday, 16

Movement:

Meals:

Sunday, 17

Movement:

Meals:

Grocery Must Haves:

April 2022

Monday, 18

Movement:

Meals:

Tuesday, 19

Movement:

Meals:

Wednesday, 20

Movement:

Meals:

Thursday, 21

Movement:

Meals:

Happy + Healthy Intention:

Movement:

Meals:

Friday, 22

Movement:

Meals:

Saturday, 23

Movement:

Meals:

Sunday, 24

Grocery Must Haves:

- ○
- ○
- ○
- ○
- ○
- ○
- ○
- ○
- ○
- ○
- ○
- ○
- ○
- ○
- ○

April 2022

Monday, 25

Movement:

Meals:

Tuesday, 26

Movement:

Meals:

Wednesday, 27

Movement:

Meals:

Thursday, 28

Movement:

Meals:

Happy + Healthy Intention:

Movement:

Meals:

Friday, 29

Movement:

Meals:

Saturday, 30

Movement:

Meals:

Sunday, 1

Grocery Must Haves:

Sunday	Monday	Tuesday
1	2	3
Mother's Day 8	9	10
15	16	17
22	23	24
29	Memorial Day 30	31

Wednesday	Thursday	Friday	Saturday
4	5	6	7
11	12	13	14
18	19	20	21
25	26	27	28

at a glance

May Goals:

May Birthdays:

May Anniversaries:

May To Do:

○
○
○
○
○
○
○
○
○

Habit Tracker

Habit	1	2	3	4	5	6	7	8	9	10	11	12	13

Less Self Doubt, More Self Love

Gratitude:

Budget:

Shopping List:

14	15	16	17	18	19	20	21	22	23	24	25	26	27	28	29	30	31

May 2022

Monday, 2

Movement:

Meals:

Tuesday, 3

Movement:

Meals:

Wednesday, 4

Movement:

Meals:

Thursday, 5

Movement:

Meals:

Happy + Healthy Intention:

Friday, 6

Movement:

Meals:

Saturday, 7

Movement:

Meals:

Sunday, 8

Movement:

Meals:

Grocery Must Haves:

May 2022

Monday, 9

•
•
•
•

Movement:

Meals:

Tuesday, 10

•
•
•
•

Movement:

Meals:

Wednesday, 11

•
•
•
•

Movement:

Meals:

Thursday, 12

•
•
•
•

Movement:

Meals:

Happy + Healthy Intention:

Friday, 13

Movement:

Meals:

Saturday, 14

Movement:

Meals:

Sunday, 15

Movement:

Meals:

Grocery Must Haves:

May 2022

Monday, 16

Movement:

Meals:

Tuesday, 17

Movement:

Meals:

Wednesday, 18

Movement:

Meals:

Thursday, 19

Movement:

Meals:

Happy + Healthy Intention:

Friday, 20

Movement:

Meals:

Saturday, 21

Movement:

Meals:

Sunday, 22

Movement:

Meals:

Grocery Must Haves:

May 2022

Monday, 23

Movement:

Meals:

Tuesday, 24

Movement:

Meals:

Wednesday, 25

Movement:

Meals:

Thursday, 26

Movement:

Meals:

Happy + Healthy Intention:

Friday, 27

Movement:

Meals:

Saturday, 28

Movement:

Meals:

Sunday, 29

Movement:

Meals:

Grocery Must Haves:

May 2022

Monday, 30

Movement:

Meals:

Tuesday, 31

Movement:

Meals:

Wednesday, 1

Movement:

Meals:

Thursday, 2

Movement:

Meals:

Happy + Healthy Intention:

Friday, 3

Movement:

Meals:

Saturday, 4

Movement:

Meals:

Sunday, 5

Movement:

Meals:

Grocery Must Haves:

Sunday	Monday	Tuesday
5	6	7
12	13	14
Juneteenth Father's Day 19	20	21
26	27	28

Wednesday	Thursday	Friday	Saturday
1	2	3	4
8	9	10	11
15	16	17	18
22	23	24	25
29	30		

June
at a glance

June Goals:

June Birthdays:

June Anniversaries:

June To Do:

○
○
○
○
○
○
○
○
○

Habit Tracker

Habit	1	2	3	4	5	6	7	8	9	10	11	12

Keep your foot on the gas

Gratitude:

Shopping List:

Budget:

13	14	15	16	17	18	19	20	21	22	23	24	25	26	27	28	29	30

June 2022

Monday, 6

•
•
•
•

Movement:

Meals:

Tuesday, 7

•
•
•
•

Movement:

Meals:

Wednesday, 8

•
•
•
•

Movement:

Meals:

Thursday, 9

•
•
•
•

Movement:

Meals:

Happy + Healthy Intention:

Movement:

Meals:

Friday, 10

Movement:

Meals:

Saturday, 11

Movement:

Meals:

Sunday, 12

Grocery Must Haves:

June 2022

Monday, 13

•
•
•
•

Movement:

Meals:

Tuesday, 14

•
•
•
•

Movement:

Meals:

Wednesday, 15

•
•
•
•

Movement:

Meals:

Thursday, 16

•
•
•
•

Movement:

Meals:

Happy + Healthy Intention:

Friday, 17

Movement:

Meals:

Saturday, 18

Movement:

Meals:

Sunday, 19

Movement:

Meals:

Grocery Must Haves:

June 2022

Monday, 20

Movement:

Meals:

Tuesday, 21

Movement:

Meals:

Wednesday, 22

Movement:

Meals:

Thursday, 23

Movement:

Meals:

Happy + Healthy Intention:

Friday, 24

Movement:

Meals:

Saturday, 25

Movement:

Meals:

Sunday, 26

Movement:

Meals:

Grocery Must Haves:

June 2022

Monday, 27

-
-
-
-

Movement:

Meals:

Tuesday, 28

-
-
-
-

Movement:

Meals:

Wednesday, 29

-
-
-
-

Movement:

Meals:

Thursday, 30

-
-
-
-

Movement:

Meals:

Happy + Healthy Intention:

Friday, 1

Movement:

Meals:

Saturday, 2

Movement:

Meals:

Sunday, 3

Movement:

Meals:

Grocery Must Haves:

Summer 2022

Be:

Quit:

Continue:

Try:

Learn:

Start:

Have:

Stop:

Quarterly Check In

What worked over the last few months?

What did not work over the last few months?

Which goal do I want to focus on this quarter?

What steps do I need to take?

How do I want to feel like at the next quarterly check in?

JULY 2022

Sunday	Monday	Tuesday
3	Independence Day 4	5
10	11	12
17	18	19
24 / 31	25	26

Wednesday	Thursday	Friday	Saturday
		1	2
6	7	8	9
13	14	15	16
20	21	22	23
27	28	29	30

July

at a glance

July Goals:

July Birthdays:

July Anniversaries:

July To Do:

- ○
- ○
- ○
- ○
- ○
- ○
- ○
- ○
- ○

Habit Tracker

Habit	1	2	3	4	5	6	7	8	9	10	11	12	13

Someday is not a day of the week

Gratitude:

Shopping List:

Budget:

14	15	16	17	18	19	20	21	22	23	24	25	26	27	28	29	30	31

July 2022

Monday, 4

-
-
-
-

Movement:

Meals:

Tuesday, 5

-
-
-
-

Movement:

Meals:

Wednesday, 6

-
-
-
-

Movement:

Meals:

Thursday, 7

-
-
-
-

Movement:

Meals:

Happy + Healthy Intention:

Friday, 8

Movement:

Meals:

Saturday, 9

Movement:

Meals:

Sunday, 10

Movement:

Meals:

Grocery Must Haves:

July 2022

Monday, 11

•
•
•
•

Movement:

Meals:

Tuesday, 12

•
•
•
•

Movement:

Meals:

Wednesday, 13

•
•
•
•

Movement:

Meals:

Thursday, 14

•
•
•
•

Movement:

Meals:

Happy + Healthy Intention:

Movement:

Meals:

Friday, 15

Movement:

Meals:

Saturday, 16

Movement:

Meals:

Sunday, 17

Grocery Must Haves:

July 2022

Monday, 18

-
-
-
-

Movement:

Meals:

Tuesday, 19

-
-
-
-

Movement:

Meals:

Wednesday, 20

-
-
-
-

Movement:

Meals:

Thursday, 21

-
-
-
-

Movement:

Meals:

Happy + Healthy Intention:

Friday, 22

Movement:

Meals:

Saturday, 23

Movement:

Meals:

Sunday, 24

Movement:

Meals:

Grocery Must Haves:

July 2022

Monday, 25

•
•
•
•

Movement:

Meals:

Tuesday, 26

•
•
•
•

Movement:

Meals:

Wednesday, 27

•
•
•
•

Movement:

Meals:

Thursday, 28

•
•
•
•

Movement:

Meals:

Happy + Healthy Intention:

Movement:

Meals:

Friday, 29

Movement:

Meals:

Saturday, 30

Movement:

Meals:

Sunday, 31

Grocery Must Haves:

AUGUST 2022

Sunday	Monday	Tuesday
	1	2
7	8	9
14	15	16
21	22	23
28	29	30

Wednesday	Thursday	Friday	Saturday
3	4	5	6
10	11	12	13
17	18	19	20
24	25	26	27
31			

August
at a glance

August Goals:

August Birthdays:

August Anniversaries:

August To Do:

- ○
- ○
- ○
- ○
- ○
- ○
- ○
- ○
- ○

Habit Tracker

Habit	1	2	3	4	5	6	7	8	9	10	11	12	13

Stay on the path that makes you most fulfilled

Gratitude:

Shopping List:

Budget:

14	15	16	17	18	19	20	21	22	23	24	25	26	27	28	29	30	31

August 2022

Monday, 1

-
-
-
-

Movement:

Meals:

Tuesday, 2

-
-
-
-

Movement:

Meals:

Wednesday, 3

-
-
-
-

Movement:

Meals:

Thursday, 4

-
-
-
-

Movement:

Meals:

Happy + Healthy Intention:

Movement:

Meals:

Friday, 5

Movement:

Meals:

Saturday, 6

Movement:

Meals:

Sunday, 7

Grocery Must Haves:

August 2022

Monday, 8

-
-
-
-

Movement:

Meals:

Tuesday, 9

-
-
-
-

Movement:

Meals:

Wednesday, 10

-
-
-
-

Movement:

Meals:

Thursday, 11

-
-
-
-

Movement:

Meals:

Happy + Healthy Intention:

Friday, 12

Movement:

Meals:

Saturday, 13

Movement:

Meals:

Sunday, 14

Movement:

Meals:

Grocery Must Haves:

August 2022

Monday, 15

-
-
-
-

Movement:

Meals:

Tuesday, 16

-
-
-
-

Movement:

Meals:

Wednesday, 17

-
-
-
-

Movement:

Meals:

Thursday, 18

-
-
-
-

Movement:

Meals:

Happy + Healthy Intention:

Friday, 19

Movement:

Meals:

Saturday, 20

Movement:

Meals:

Sunday, 21

Movement:

Meals:

Grocery Must Haves:

August 2022

Monday, 22

•
•
•
•

Movement:

Meals:

Tuesday, 23

•
•
•
•

Movement:

Meals:

Wednesday, 24

•
•
•
•

Movement:

Meals:

Thursday, 25

•
•
•
•

Movement:

Meals:

Happy + Healthy Intention:

Friday, 26

Movement:

Meals:

Saturday, 27

Movement:

Meals:

Sunday, 28

Movement:

Meals:

Grocery Must Haves:

August 2022

Monday, 29

•
•
•
•

Movement:

Meals:

Tuesday, 30

•
•
•
•

Movement:

Meals:

Wednesday, 31

•
•
•
•

Movement:

Meals:

Thursday, 1

•
•
•
•

Movement:

Meals:

Happy + Healthy Intention:

Friday, 2

Movement:

Meals:

Saturday, 3

Movement:

Meals:

Sunday, 4

Movement:

Meals:

Grocery Must Haves:

Sunday	Monday	Tuesday
4	Labor Day 5	6
11	12	13
18	19	20
25	26	27

Wednesday	Thursday	Friday	Saturday
	1	2	3
7	8	9	10
14	15	16	17
21	22	23	24
28	29	30	

September
at a glance

September Goals:

September Birthdays:

September Anniversaries:

September To Do:

○
○
○
○
○
○
○
○
○

Habit Tracker

Habit	1	2	3	4	5	6	7	8	9	10	11	12

The secret of your future is hidden in your daily routine

Gratitude:

Shopping List:

Budget:

13	14	15	16	17	18	19	20	21	22	23	24	25	26	27	28	29	30

September 2022

Monday, 5

-
-
-
-

Movement:

Meals:

Tuesday, 6

-
-
-
-

Movement:

Meals:

Wednesday, 7

-
-
-
-

Movement:

Meals:

Thursday, 8

-
-
-
-

Movement:

Meals:

Happy + Healthy Intention:

Friday, 9

Movement:

Meals:

Saturday, 10

Movement:

Meals:

Sunday, 11

Movement:

Meals:

Grocery Must Haves:

September 2022

Monday, 12

•
•
•
•

Movement:

Meals:

Tuesday, 13

•
•
•
•

Movement:

Meals:

Wednesday, 14

•
•
•
•

Movement:

Meals:

Thursday, 15

•
•
•
•

Movement:

Meals:

Happy + Healthy Intention:

Friday, 16

Movement:

Meals:

Saturday, 17

Movement:

Meals:

Sunday, 18

Movement:

Meals:

Grocery Must Haves:

September 2022

Monday, 19

•
•
•
•

Movement:

Meals:

Tuesday, 20

•
•
•
•

Movement:

Meals:

Wednesday, 21

•
•
•
•

Movement:

Meals:

Thursday, 22

•
•
•
•

Movement:

Meals:

Happy + Healthy Intention:

Friday, 23

Movement:

Meals:

Saturday, 24

Movement:

Meals:

Sunday, 25

Movement:

Meals:

Grocery Must Haves:

September 2022

Monday, 26

-
-
-
-

Movement:

Meals:

Tuesday, 27

-
-
-
-

Movement:

Meals:

Wednesday, 28

-
-
-
-

Movement:

Meals:

Thursday, 29

-
-
-
-

Movement:

Meals:

Happy + Healthy Intention:

Friday, 30

-
-
-
-

Movement:

Meals:

Saturday, 1

-
-
-

Movement:

Meals:

Sunday, 2

-
-
-

Movement:

Meals:

Grocery Must Haves:

- ○
- ○
- ○
- ○
- ○
- ○
- ○
- ○
- ○
- ○
- ○
- ○
- ○
- ○
- ○

Fall 2022

Be:

Quit:

Continue:

Try:

Learn:

Start:

Have:

Stop:

Quarterly Check In

What worked over the last few months?

What did not work over the last few months?

Which goal do I want to focus on this quarter?

What steps do I need to take?

How do I want to feel like at the next quarterly check in?

OCTOBER 2022

Sunday	Monday	Tuesday
2	3	4
9	10	11
16	17	18
23 30	24 Halloween 31	25

Wednesday	Thursday	Friday	Saturday
			1
5	6	7	8
12	13	14	15
19	20	21	22
26	27	28	29

October

at a glance

October Goals:

October Birthdays:

October Anniversaries:

October To Do:

○
○
○
○
○
○
○
○
○

Habit Tracker

Habit	1	2	3	4	5	6	7	8	9	10	11	12	13

Kindness always comes back

Gratitude:

Shopping List:

Budget:

14	15	16	17	18	19	20	21	22	23	24	25	26	27	28	29	30	31

October 2022

Monday, 3

Movement:

Meals:

Tuesday, 4

Movement:

Meals:

Wednesday, 5

Movement:

Meals:

Thursday, 6

Movement:

Meals:

Happy + Healthy Intention:

Friday, 7

Movement:

Meals:

Saturday, 8

Movement:

Meals:

Sunday, 9

Movement:

Meals:

Grocery Must Haves:

October 2022

Monday, 10

Movement:

Meals:

Tuesday, 11

Movement:

Meals:

Wednesday, 12

Movement:

Meals:

Thursday, 13

Movement:

Meals:

Happy + Healthy Intention:

Movement:

Meals:

Friday, 14

Movement:

Meals:

Saturday, 15

Movement:

Meals:

Sunday, 16

Grocery Must Haves:

○ ○ ○
○ ○ ○
○ ○ ○
○ ○ ○
○ ○ ○

October 2022

Monday, 17

Movement:

Meals:

Tuesday, 18

Movement:

Meals:

Wednesday, 19

Movement:

Meals:

Thursday, 20

Movement:

Meals:

Happy + Healthy Intention:

Friday, 21

Movement:

Meals:

Saturday, 22

Movement:

Meals:

Sunday, 23

Movement:

Meals:

Grocery Must Haves:

October 2022

Monday, 24

Movement:

Meals:

Tuesday, 25

Movement:

Meals:

Wednesday, 26

Movement:

Meals:

Thursday, 27

Movement:

Meals:

Happy + Healthy Intention:

Movement:

Meals:

Friday, 28

Movement:

Meals:

Saturday, 29

Movement:

Meals:

Sunday, 30

Grocery Must Haves:

October 2022

Monday, 31

Movement:

Meals:

Tuesday, 1

Movement:

Meals:

Wednesday, 2

Movement:

Meals:

Thursday, 3

Movement:

Meals:

Happy + Healthy Intention:

Movement:

Meals:

Friday, 4

Movement:

Meals:

Saturday, 5

Movement:

Meals:

Sunday, 6

Grocery Must Haves:

NOVEMBER 2022

Sunday	Monday	Tuesday
		1
6	7	8
13	14	15
20	21	22
27	28	29

Wednesday	Thursday	Friday	Saturday
2	3	4	5
9	10	Veterans Day 11	12
16	17	18	19
23	Thanksgiving 24	25	26
30			

November
at a glance

November Goals:

November Birthdays:

November Anniversaries:

November To Do:

○
○
○
○
○
○
○
○
○

Habit Tracker

Habit	1	2	3	4	5	6	7	8	9	10	11	12

Let's see what happens when you don't give up

Gratitude:

Shopping List:

Budget:

13	14	15	16	17	18	19	20	21	22	23	24	25	26	27	28	29	30

November 2022

Monday, 7

-
-
-
-

Movement:

Meals:

Tuesday, 8

-
-
-
-

Movement:

Meals:

Wednesday, 9

-
-
-
-

Movement:

Meals:

Thursday, 10

-
-
-
-

Movement:

Meals:

Happy + Healthy Intention:

Friday, 11

Movement:

Meals:

Saturday, 12

Movement:

Meals:

Sunday, 13

Movement:

Meals:

Grocery Must Haves:

November 2022

Monday, 14

Movement:

Meals:

Tuesday, 15

Movement:

Meals:

Wednesday, 16

Movement:

Meals:

Thursday, 17

Movement:

Meals:

Happy + Healthy Intention:

Friday, 18

Movement:

Meals:

Saturday, 19

Movement:

Meals:

Sunday, 20

Movement:

Meals:

Grocery Must Haves:

November 2022

Monday, 21

Movement:

Meals:

Tuesday, 22

Movement:

Meals:

Wednesday, 23

Movement:

Meals:

Thursday, 24

Movement:

Meals:

Happy + Healthy Intention:

Movement:

Meals:

Friday, 25

Movement:

Meals:

Saturday, 26

Movement:

Meals:

Sunday, 27

Grocery Must Haves:

November 2022

Monday, 28

Movement:

Meals:

Tuesday, 29

Movement:

Meals:

Wednesday, 30

Movement:

Meals:

Thursday, 1

Movement:

Meals:

Happy + Healthy Intention:

Friday, 2

Movement:

Meals:

Saturday, 3

Movement:

Meals:

Sunday, 4

Movement:

Meals:

Grocery Must Haves:

Sunday	Monday	Tuesday
4	5	6
11	12	13
Hanukkah Begins 18	19	20
Christmas 25	Hanukkah Ends 26	27

Wednesday	Thursday	Friday	Saturday
	1	2	3
7	8	9	10
14	15	16	17
21	22	23	Christmas Eve 24
28	29	30	New Year's Eve 31

December
at a glance

December Goals:

December Birthdays:

December Anniversaries:

December To Do:

○
○
○
○
○
○
○
○
○

Habit Tracker

Habit	1	2	3	4	5	6	7	8	9	10	11	12	13

Don't wait for happiness - create it

Gratitude:

Shopping List:

Budget:

14	15	16	17	18	19	20	21	22	23	24	25	26	27	28	29	30	31

December 2022

Monday, 5

-
-
-
-

Movement:

Meals:

Tuesday, 6

-
-
-
-

Movement:

Meals:

Wednesday, 7

-
-
-
-

Movement:

Meals:

Thursday, 8

-
-
-
-

Movement:

Meals:

Happy + Healthy Intention:

Friday, 9

Movement:

Meals:

Saturday, 10

Movement:

Meals:

Sunday, 11

Movement:

Meals:

Grocery Must Haves:

December 2022

Monday, 12

-
-
-
-

Movement:

Meals:

Tuesday, 13

-
-
-
-

Movement:

Meals:

Wednesday, 14

-
-
-
-

Movement:

Meals:

Thursday, 15

-
-
-
-

Movement:

Meals:

Happy + Healthy Intention:

Friday, 16

Movement:

Meals:

Saturday, 17

Movement:

Meals:

Sunday, 18

Movement:

Meals:

Grocery Must Haves:

December 2022

Monday, 19

•
•
•
•

Movement:

Meals:

Tuesday, 20

•
•
•
•

Movement:

Meals:

Wednesday, 21

•
•
•
•

Movement:

Meals:

Thursday, 22

•
•
•
•

Movement:

Meals:

Happy + Healthy Intention:

Friday, 23

Movement:

Meals:

Saturday, 24

Movement:

Meals:

Sunday, 25

Movement:

Meals:

Grocery Must Haves:

December 2022

Monday, 26

•
•
•
•

Movement:

Meals:

Tuesday, 27

•
•
•
•

Movement:

Meals:

Wednesday, 28

•
•
•
•

Movement:

Meals:

Thursday, 29

•
•
•
•

Movement:

Meals:

Happy + Healthy Intention:

Friday, 30

Movement:

Meals:

Saturday, 31

Movement:

Meals:

Sunday, 1

Movement:

Meals:

Grocery Must Haves:

2022 In Review

Be:

Quit:

Continue:

Try:

Learn:

Start:

Have:

Stop:

Final Check In

What worked this year for me?

What did not work this year for me?

What goals do I want to carry into next year?

What steps do I need to take?

How do I want to feel one year from now?

Notes:

Notes:

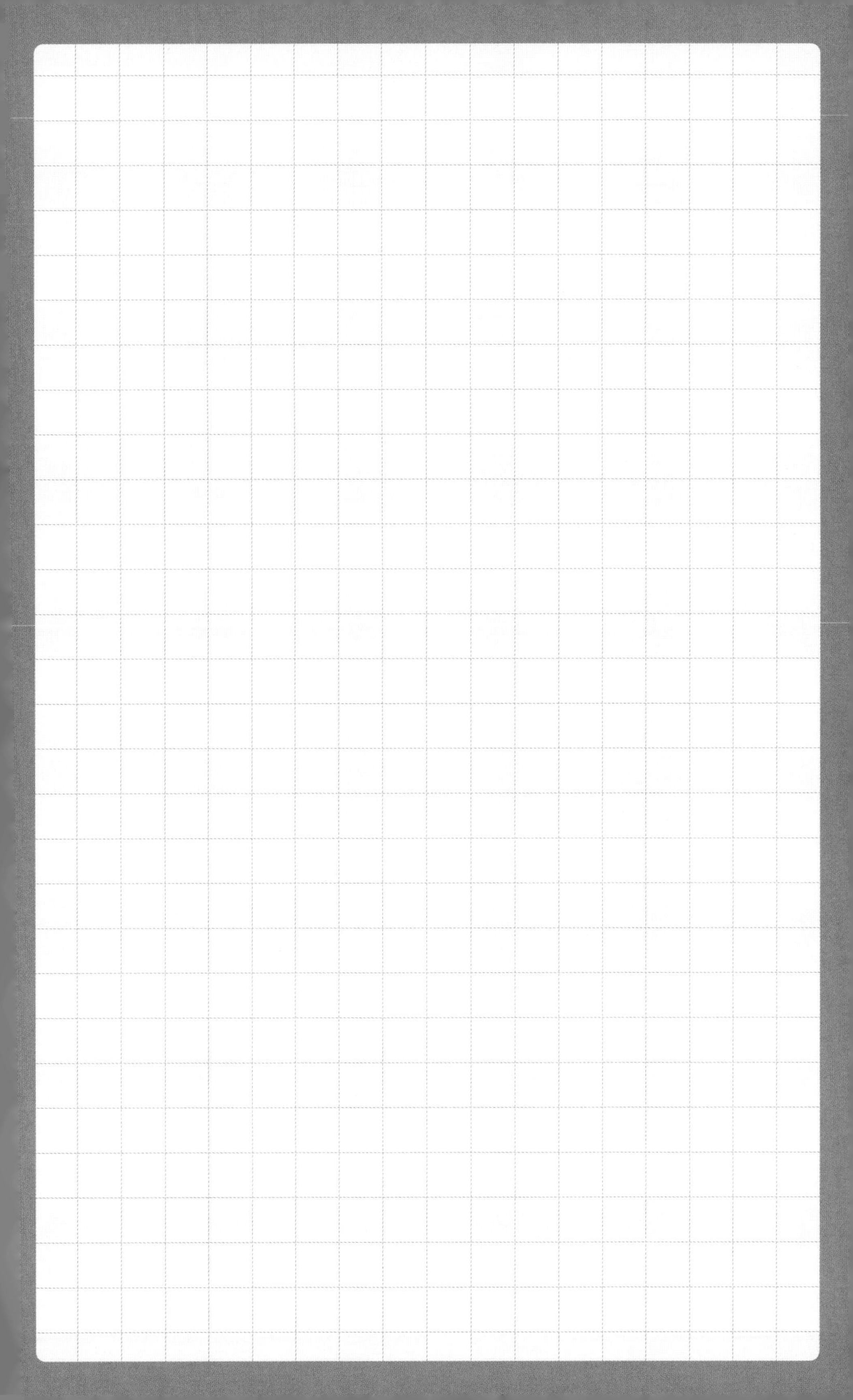

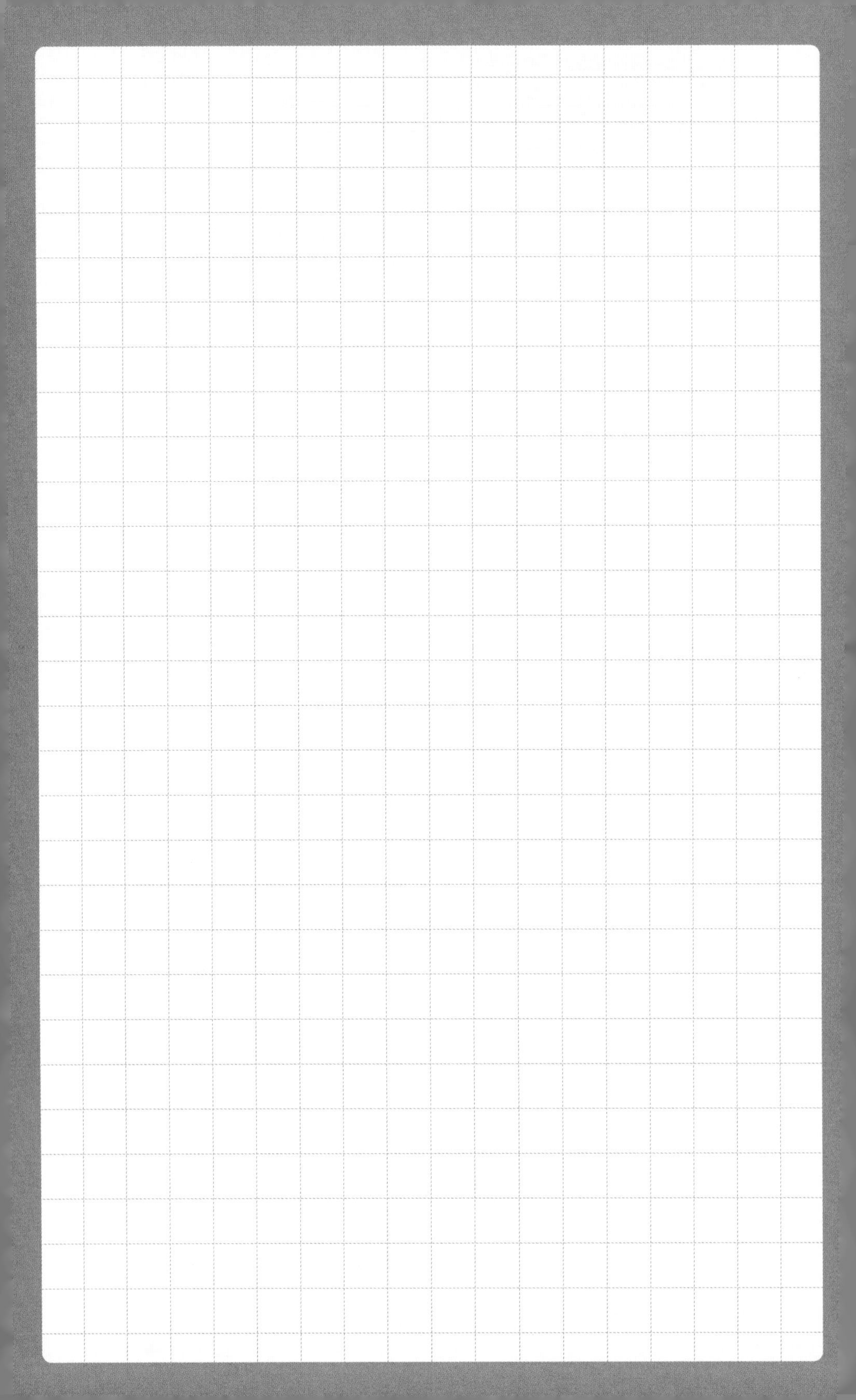

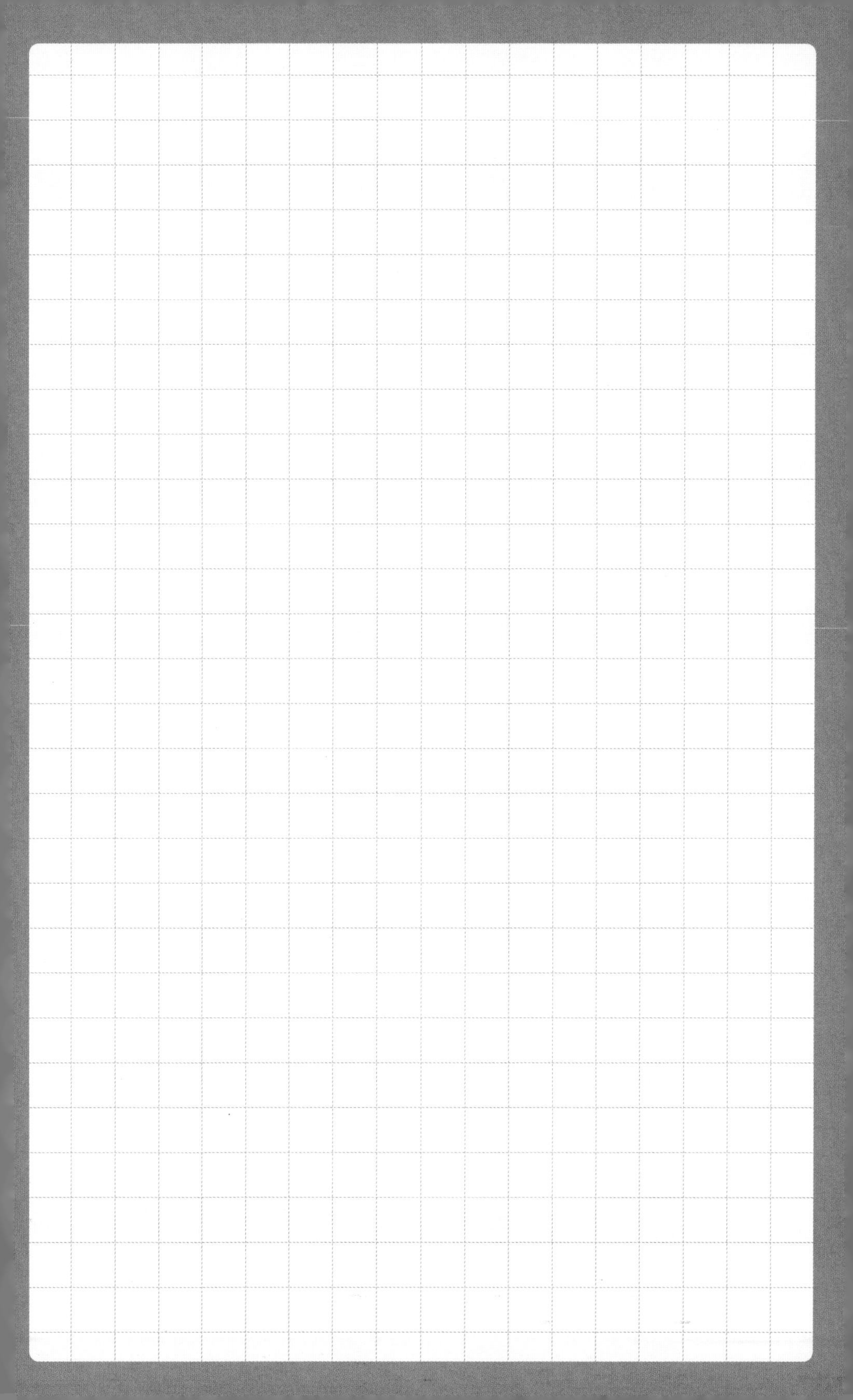

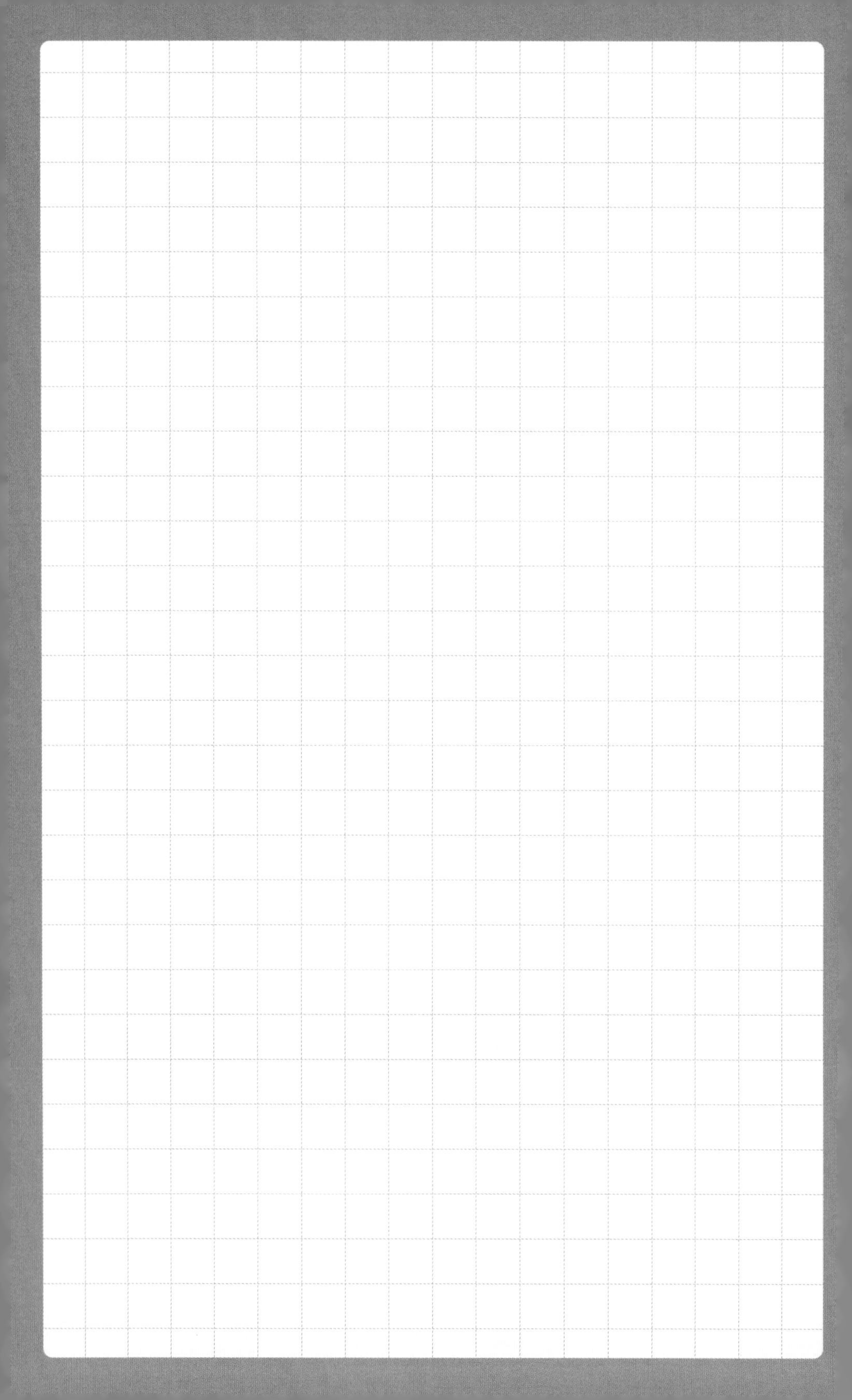

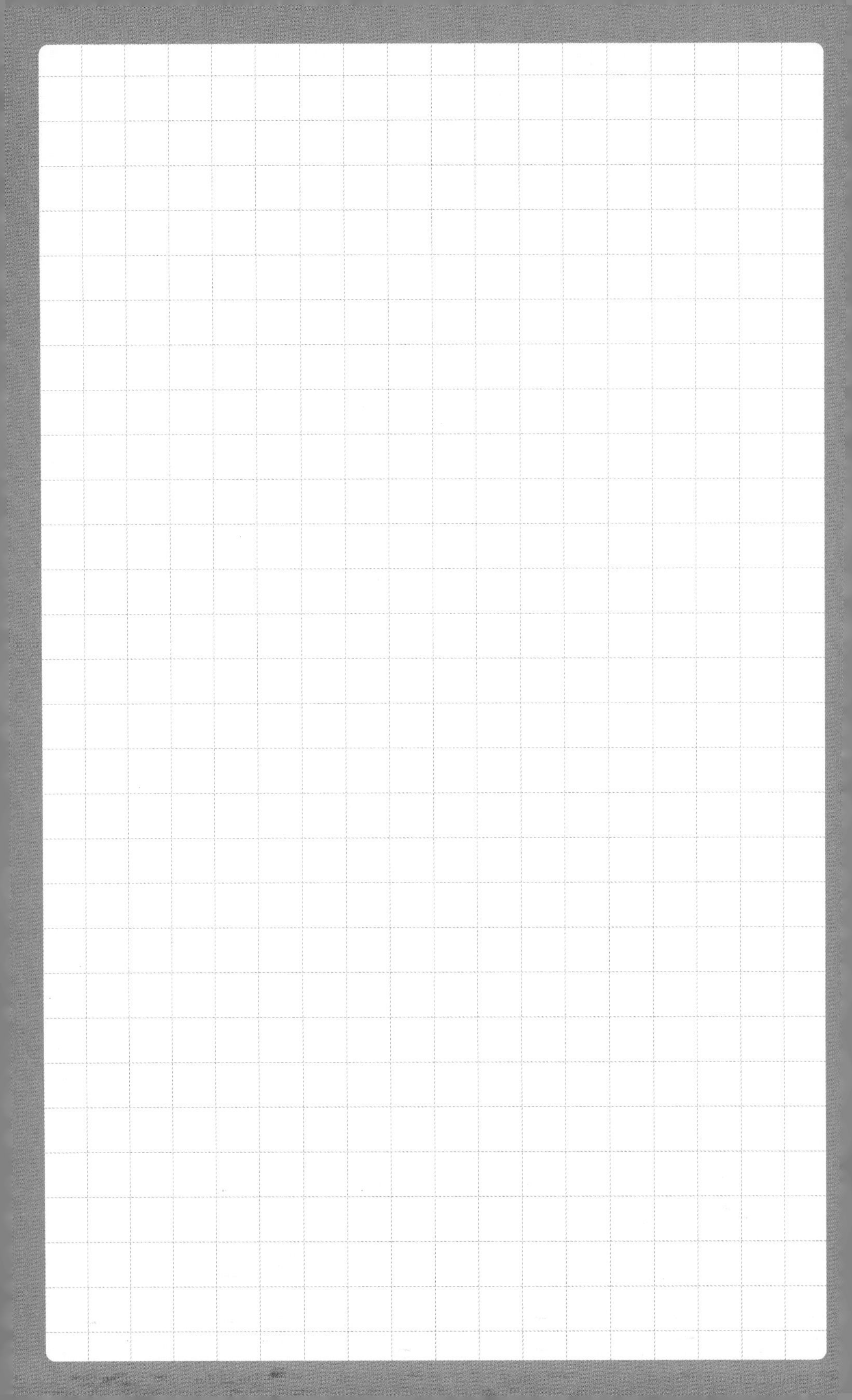

Happy + Healthy 2022 Planner

Hello new year, new you!
This planner will become your best friend, your life guide, your source of inspiration, and your motivational cheerleader all in one.

I created the first Happy + Healthy planner in 2021 as a one-stop tool to encompass both your "real life" and your "wellness life." Because at the end of the day, isn't the goal to make them one and the same? This 2022 version has the areas you love, like the At A Glance page & Habit Tracker, plus Daily Workouts and Eats. It also has extended areas for Weekly Grocery Lists, Monthly Motivating Quotes (not too cheesy, I swear) & Quarterly Resolution Check In's. Get ready to live your happiest & healthiest life yet.

Xoxo,

(@skinnyhangover)